D1454530

Forces and moveme...

Contents

Teachers' notes	1	The effect of rubber on friction?	19
Forces at work	5	Liquids and friction	20
Pushes and pulls	6	Can friction be used to warm water?	21
Small forces	7	Using rollers	22
Balanced and unbalanced forces	8	The balloon in a box	23
Feeling forces	9	How do ball-bearings help movement?	24
Falling objects	10	Floating cans	25
Investigating gravity	11	Floating balls	26
A simple weighing machine	12	Measuring floating forces	27
Weighing with a squashed spring	13	Make a paddle boat	28
Pendulums and swings	14	Magnetic forces	29
Make a wind brake	15	How strong is a magnet?	30
Does size affect a parachute's speed?	16	Levers	31
Measure the force of the wind	17	See-saw	32
Is friction useful or a nuisance?	18		

Teachers' notes

Aims of this book

• To let the children explore the properties of forces including magnetism; how they push and pull, make things move, stop, change speed or direction, and how they change the shape of objects.
• To show that objects have weight because of the gravitational attraction between them and the Earth.
• To show that forces act in particular directions and that pairs of forces can balance or be unbalanced.
• To show that magnets exert a force. The force of magnetism only works between two magnets and objects made of iron, steel, cobalt and nickel.

Developing science skills

While it is not essential to follow the order of the worksheets in this book, all those covering one aspect of the subject, such as gravity or magnetism, should be dealt with at approximately the same time.

Although it is in the *doing* of science that children learn best, this involves more than just practical work. They need to observe, record and predict, measure, look for patterns, classify, explain and ask questions that can lead to further investigations. They need time to discuss their work, before and after the activity: this will also aid the teacher in monitoring the children's progress so that they build a valid framework for future development.

For those children who lack the necessary reading skills, it is suggested that you read the sheet with them and, by careful questioning, establish whether or not the instructions have been understood.

Safety precautions

Encourage good, safe habits when lifting heavy objects.
Warn children of the dangers to the eyes and face from overstretched rubber bands and springs.
Do not leave marbles or ball-bearings on the floor.
Take care when dropping balls and other objects.

Scientific background

This information aims to help you to understand the scientific ideas covered in this book. It generally goes beyond the level of understanding of most children, but will give you the confidence to ask and answer questions and to guide the children's investigations.

Forces

A force is simply a push, a pull or a twist. It may move something, stop it or change its speed or direction. It may even squeeze an object and change its shape.

Every type of movement is caused by a force yet forces are invisible. Stationary objects resist moving (inertia), so a force, usually a push or a pull, is always needed to start movement. The amount needed depends on several factors: the mass and volume of the object, what it is made from, the material through which it will travel and the surface on which it is resting. The stronger a force, the stronger its effects. For every force there is an equal and opposite... e other, something ... er bridge or some ... ll collapse. If the ... stay still.

▲ ESSENTIALS FOR SCIENCE: Forces and movement

Friction

Friction is the force that may exist between two surfaces and tends to prevent movement. It acts against any force which may cause movement. If the push or pull is greater than the opposing frictional force, movement will occur. If the frictional force equals the push or pull, there will be no movement.

The lower the force of friction between two surfaces, the easier sliding movement between them becomes. The higher the force of friction, the easier it is to stop sliding. Friction between a vehicle's wheels and the road surface actually helps the forward motion of the vehicle. Without this friction the wheels would simply spin round. Friction also lets our shoes grip the floor when we walk, it keeps nails and screws in wood, stops ladders falling over and allows brakes to stop motor vehicles and bicycles.

Weight and gravity

Since objects fall to the ground, there must be a force pulling them down. This is gravity and it pulls objects towards the centre of the Earth. The amount of force pulling people and objects down like this is what we call weight. In space, there is very little gravity and things float about freely.

The gas particles which make up the air have to be pushed out of the way of falling objects. The larger the object, the more air it has to push out of the way and so the longer it tends to take to reach the ground. The force of the air particles against the surface of the falling object is one of friction.

Although we talk about measuring weight in pounds or kilograms, these are really units of mass – the amount of substance in something. When measuring forces, including weight, we should use a unit called a newton. On Earth, the gravitational pull on a 100g mass is about 1 newton, that is, the weight of 100g mass is 1 newton. The newton is named after Sir Issac Newton whose important discoveries about forces helped lay the foundations of modern science.

Magnetism

Magnetism only works between two magnets, or a magnet and certain metal objects. The most common magnetic metal is iron, or steel which is an alloy of it.

Finally, it should be remembered that wheels, pulleys and levers reduce the amount of work needed to harness the forces mentioned here.

Notes on individual activities

Page 5: Forces at work
Key idea: a force is a push, a pull or a twist.
Likely outcome: the wheelbarrow, ball and bulldozer are moved by pushing; the dog is pulling its owner; the jar lid is removed by twisting; the door is opened by twisting the knob and then is either pushed or pulled depending on its fixing. The biggest force is the bulldozer.
Extension: collect objects which can be pushed, pulled or twisted and use these to investigate further.

Page 6: Pushes and pulls
Key idea: It is possible to change the direction of movement caused by a push or pull.
Likely outcome: the truck will move towards the girl when she pulls it. When the string is around the tree, as she pulls the rope the truck will move away from her. The same principle applies to a push. By putting a hand on the far side of the book, you can push it towards you; by gripping the far side of the book you can pull it away from you.
Extension: see how push and pull forces can change the shape of clay or Plasticine.

Page 7: Small forces

Key idea: a small force can move light objects, while heavy objects are only moved by a large force.
Likely outcome: very heavy objects are not moved by either blowing or gentle pushing. You only need a small force to move light objects.
Extension: list objects in the home which are moved by pushing, pulling or twisting.

Page 8: Balanced and unbalanced forces

Key ideas: if two forces balance, things stay still. If forces are unbalanced, then movement occurs.
Likely outcome: the balanced forces are likely to be the children pulling the cracker, the tug-of-war teams and the ship floating in water (the upthrust of the water equals the downward push of the ship's weight, thus keeping the ship afloat). The other pictures show unbalanced forces.

Page 9: Feeling forces

Key ideas: the pull of gravity gives us a sense of 'up' and 'down'. Gravity also gives a measure of weight.
Likely outcome: the larger the object, the bigger its downward force and the harder it pulls the hand down.
Extension: try to estimate the weight of small objects by comparing them with known weights.

Page 10: Falling objects

Key idea: to explore the pull of gravity.
Likely outcome: the objects will all fall at the same rate. Only objects which have a larger surface area and therefore offer more resistance to the air (feather, sheet of paper) will fall more slowly.
Extension: make a paper dart or aeroplane to demonstrate the idea of air resistance.

Page 11: Investigating gravity

Key ideas: as objects fall to Earth, the speed at which they fall accelerates. Objects that fall greater distances have time to reach a greater speed, therefore increasing the impact on landing.
Likely outcome: the further the balls have fallen, the more they will have been damaged by the impact with the floor. Gravity makes all four balls accelerate uniformly, but the ball which has fallen the greatest distance has had time to reach the greatest speed, and therefore will show the greatest damage.

Extension: investigate whether pushing an object makes it fall faster than just dropping it.

Page 12: A simple weighing machine

Key ideas: objects have weight because gravity pulls on them. Rubber will stretch under the influence of a force and, provided the elastic limit is not reached, will return to its original shape.

Likely outcome: the heavier the object hung on the elastic band, the more it will stretch. There is an 'elastic limit' beyond which the rubber either loses its elasticity or breaks.

Extension: make weighing machines using thin springs instead of elastic bands.

Safety precautions: take care to avoid eye and facial injuries from stretched elastic bands or springs.

Page 13: Weighing with a squashed spring

Key idea: the heavier the object placed on a spring, the more it is compressed.

Likely outcome: as long as the elastic limit is not reached, the heavier the object placed in the small can, the more the spring will be compressed.

Extension: examine various weighing machines, (eg. kitchen scales, spring balances and bathroom scales) to see how they work.

Page 14: Pendulums and swings

Key ideas: the longer a pendulum, the more slowly it swings. A weight on the end makes no difference.

Likely outcome: the 60cm pendulum takes three times as long for each swing as the 20cm one. The weight on the end makes no difference to the number of times the pendulum swings each minute.

Extension: look at swings in the local playground. Do they behave in the same way as pendulums?

Page 15: Make a wind brake

Key idea: the friction of the air can slow movement.

Likely outcome: the cotton reel turns more slowly with the pieces of card in place. Gravity makes the paper-clips fall, pull the string and turn the reel. Air pushes against the pieces of card, reducing its speed.

Extension: examine pictures of air brakes on aircraft to see how they work. Make a paper aircraft with air brakes on its wings.

Safety precautions: an adult should cut the slits in the cotton reel with a small saw or an old bread knife.

Page 16: Does size affect a parachute's speed?

Key ideas: objects push against the air as the force of gravity causes them to fall. Objects with a large surface have more air resistance.

Likely outcome: the larger parachute opens and floats to the ground more slowly than the smaller parachute. If the parachute has a very large surface and a small weight, the upward push of air can equal the downward force, causing the parachute to float gently downward like a feather.

Extension: repeat the experiment with even larger and smaller parachutes. What is the best size of parachute to carry a steel washer?

Safety precautions: if possible, carry out the experiment in the middle of the playing field or playground, away from windows and overhead wires.

Page 17: Measure the force of the wind

Key ideas: the wind exerts a force which is variable.

Likely outcome: the harder the wind blows, the higher it pushes the flap. The scale can be calibrated using the Beaufort scale of wind speed.

Extension: discuss how the force of the wind is used in windmills, wind generators and sailing boats.

Page 18: Is friction useful or a nuisance?

Key idea: friction can be both beneficial and harmful.

Likely outcome: the rider crouches low and wears a streamlined helmet to reduce air resistance. Cogs, chain and gears are lubricated with oil to reduce friction and consequent wear. Brake pads and tyres need as much friction as possible to give grip. Pedals and handlebars have a rough covering to increase the friction between them and the rider's feet and hands.

Extension: investigate how friction is (a) harmful, and (b) useful, in a motor car.

Page 19: The effect of rubber on friction

Key idea: rubber on a surface increases the amount of friction that that surface can exert.

Likely outcome: the piece of wood is always more difficult to move when the elastic bands are in place. This is because the elastic bands increase the friction between the piece of wood and the top of the table.

Extension: does the amount of friction increase with more elastic bands around the wood? Discuss why tyres and rubber-soled footwear have tread patterns.

Page 20: Liquids and friction

Key idea: liquids, like gases and solids, exert a frictional force on objects moving through them.

Likely outcome: the tacks will generally fall to the bottom of the bottle of water much quicker than in the bottle of washing-up liquid. Friction between the tacks and the water is less than between the tacks and the washing-up liquid because water is less dense ('thinner') than washing-up liquid. Treacle, syrup and oil are even more dense and would produce even greater friction, so slowing up the tacks even more.

The tacks can be picked up with a magnet. They can also be retrieved using a sieve or tea strainer.

Extension: examine the use of oil to reduce friction in, say, a roller-skate. Measure how far it will travel down a slope before and after lubricating its wheels.

Page 21: Can friction be used to warm water?

Key idea: friction produces heat.

Likely outcome: the friction of the tape on the tin can will warm the water inside by a few degrees. The water can be made quite hot if a rota of children is arranged to pull the tape backwards and forwards.

Friction is used to make heat when people rub their hands together to warm them, and when a matchhead is rubbed against the side of a matchbox to heat up the chemicals in the matchhead.
Safety precautions: take care with thermometers.

Page 22: Using rollers

Key ideas: friction increases as the area in contact increases. Rollers and wheels reduce friction by decreasing the area of the two surfaces in contact.
Likely outcome: the rubber band stretches more when the bottom book is in direct contact with the table than when it is placed on the pencils.
Extension: repeat the experiment using LEGO wheels attached to a plastic base. What advantages do wheels have over rollers?

Page 22: The balloon in a box

Key ideas: moving air can create a force. Rollers reduce friction and make movement easier.
Likely outcome: the air rushing from the balloon pushes against the air around it and moves the box and balloon forward. The box will travel further with the drinking straw rollers in place because it has less contact with the ground and, therefore, less friction.
Extension: try this again on different floor surfaces.

Page 24: How do ball-bearings help movement?

Key idea: ball-bearings make movement easier by reducing friction.
Likely outcome: it is very difficult to spin the smaller tin on its own. When resting on the ball-bearings the tin can be spun quite easily. Lubricating these with usually makes the movement even easier.

Ball-bearings are used in bicycle handlebars and wheels to reduce friction, thus reducing the effort needed to move these parts. They are used in some moving parts of car engines for the same reason.
Extension: find out how ice-skates are lubricated as the skater moves along.

Page 25: Floating cans

Key ideas: adding weights to a floating object increases the downward force until eventually the object sinks. Floating objects displace water.
Likely outcome: as weights are added, the can sinks lower and the water level in the bowl rises. Eventually the can sinks.
Extension: repeat the experiment using salt water. Read about the function of the Plimsoll line on ships.

Page 26: Floating balls

Key ideas: water exerts an upthrust on floating objects. Floating objects displace water.
Likely outcome: the harder the ball is pressed into the water, the harder the water seems to push it upwards and the more the water level in the bucket rises. The larger ball has to be pushed hardest as it has to displace the most water.
Extension: discuss life-jackets and buoyancy aids.

Page 27: Measuring floating forces

Key idea: objects weigh less in water than in air because of the upthrust of the water.
Likely outcome: each of the objects will weigh less in water than it does in air. The greatest loss in weight will be by the largest object, as this displaces most water.
Extension: discuss the discoveries of Archimedes.

Page 28: Make a paddle boat

Key idea: when an object is pushed, it pushes back with an equal and opposite force.
Likely outcome: the boat moves forwards first and backwards when the paddle is turned the other way.
Extension: ask the children to feel what happens when they sit in a small cart and push gently against a wall.

Page 29: Magnetic forces

Key ideas: only some metals are magnetic. Like poles of magnets repel, unlike poles attract.
Likely outcome: magnets attract iron, nickel, cobalt and most types of steel. Only the nail, pin and paper-clip are likely to have been attracted. Two North poles or two South poles repel each other. Two unlike poles (North/South or South/North) attract.
Extension: will the force of a magnet pass through different materials, eg. paper, card, plastic or glass? Use paper-clips to test where a magnet is strongest.

Page 30: How strong is a magnet?

Key ideas: magnets have varying strengths. These can be compared by seeing how much they can pick up.
Likely outcome: the number of paper-clips needed to make them all fall will vary with different magnets.
Extension: test through how many sheets of paper different magnets will attract a paper-clip.

Page 31: Levers

Key ideas: levers make things easier to move as they allow a force to be applied at a distance from a pivot. A lever can amplify a force, so a small force can balance a large one provided the small force is much further from the fulcrum (pivot) than the large one.
Likely outcome: the lid and the nail are impossible to remove by hand. The lid can probably be removed with the coin, but it is easier with the screwdriver which acts as a long lever. The claw hammer also acts as a lever, making the removal of the nail easy.
Extension: explore how heavy loads can be lifted by using a plank of wood as a lever.
Safety precautions: careful supervision will be necessary when hammering nails into wood.

Page 32: See-saw

Key idea: to show how objects of unequal weight can be made to balance.
Likely outcome: the coins balance because they are an equal distance from the fulcum. Work = force × distance, so two coins 4cm from the fulcrum will balance one coin 8cm from the fulcrum.
Extension: repeat this test on a real see-saw.

▲ Name _____

Forces at work

[ ]

You will need: a pencil.

A force is a push, a pull or a twist.
A force is always needed to move something.

▲ Look at these pictures. What is moving?
Is a push, a pull or a twist moving it?
Or is it more than one of these forces?

[ ]

[ ]   [ ]

▲ Which of the pictures
shows the biggest force?

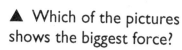
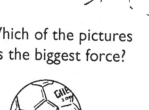

[ ]

[ ]

▲ Draw things you push, pull or twist every
day. Make a table like this:

object	push	pull	twist
comb.		x	

Pushes and pulls

You will need: a book; a cotton reel; string; a large nail knocked into the middle of a piece of wood.

Does a push always move things away? Does a pull always move things nearer?

▲ Look at this picture? The girl is pulling the string. Which way does the truck move?

▲ Now lay the book on the table. Using only one hand, can you push the book so that it moves nearer to you? Can you pull the book so that it moves away from you?

▲ Can you use the piece of string, the cotton reel and the nail in the piece of wood to pull the book away from you?

▲ In this picture the girl is also pulling. Which way does the truck move?

Small forces

You will need: a variety of everyday classroom objects; drinking straws or narrow strips of scrap paper.

One of the smallest forces you can create is by blowing.

▲ Look around your classroom. Which objects can you move by blowing? Draw a chart like the one below.

BLOWING FORCE

Objects which move when you blow lightly	Objects which move when you blow hard	Objects not moved at all by blowing
feather		

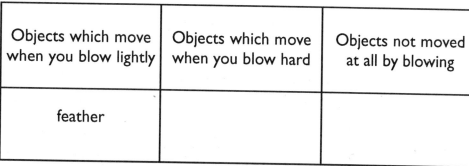

▲ Use a drinking straw or fold a strip of scrap paper in half lengthwise. Use the straw or paper to push different objects. Draw a chart like the one below.

SMALL PUSHES

Objects which move when pushed	Objects which change shape when pushed	Objects which are not affected by the push
		brick

▲ Complete these sentences:

Very _____ objects are not moved by either blowing or gentle pushing.

You only need a _____ force to move light objects.

Balanced and unbalanced forces

You will need: a pencil.

▲ Look at each of the pictures.
Are the forces in each picture balanced
or unbalanced? How do you know?

▲ Think about the direction
of the forces shown in each
of the pictures. Against each
one draw a large arrow to
show a large force and a small
arrow to show a small force.
  Make the arrows the same
size if the pair of forces are
balanced.

Feeling forces

You will need: a collection of small objects such as an apple, a book, a shoe, a pebble and a brick; a scarf or a blindfold.

▲ Conduct this experiment to see if you can 'feel' forces. Work with a friend.

1. Close your eyes or ask your friend to blindfold you.
2. Ask your friend to arrange the objects in a row in front of you.
3. Pick up the objects one at a time and 'feel' the force each one makes.

▲ In which direction are these forces acting?

4. Now try to arrange the objects in order from the biggest force to the smallest. Remove your blindfold then write down this order of objects.
5. Now blindfold your friend.
6. Rearrange the objects in a different order.
7. Ask your friend to feel each force and to arrange the objects in order.

▲ Is your friend's order the same as yours?   ▲ How can you check to see who is right?

▲ Name _____

Falling objects

You will need: several small objects, such as a marble, a pebble and a tennis ball; a large metal tray; a chair.

▲ Do some objects fall faster then others? Work with a friend to find out.

1. Hold each of the objects in turn.
2. Guess which one will fall the fastest if you drop it.
3. Place the metal tray on the ground.
4. Stand on the chair and hold two of the objects high above the tray.
5. Let go of the objects at the same time.
6. Ask your friend to see which one hits the tray first.
7. Repeat the experiment with each pair of objects.
• What do you discover?

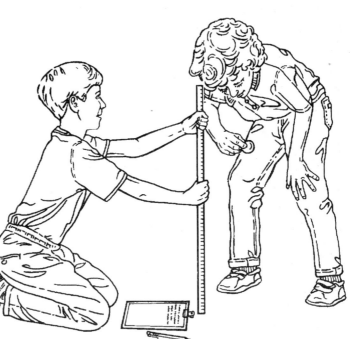

▲ Name _____

Investigating gravity

You will need: Plasticine; a tape measure; a chair to stand on.

▲ Conduct this experiment. Ask a friend to help you.

1. Make four balls with the Plasticine. Make sure that they are all the same size.
2. Drop one of the balls to the floor from a height of 50 centimetres (ask your friend to measure with a tape measure).

3. Carefully pick up the ball and put it on a piece of paper marked number 1.
4. Drop the second ball from a height of 1 metre. Call this number 2.
5. Drop the other two balls from 150 centimetres (number 3) and 2 metres (number 4).
6. Examine all four balls carefully. Can you see any difference between them?

▲ Describe what has happened to each of the balls. Can you explain what you see?

_____

_____

_____

_____

A simple weighing machine

You will need: a thick elastic band; a drawing pin; paper-clips; yoghurt pot; thin string; ruler; adhesive tape; marble; eraser; small pebble.

1. Push the drawing pin into the edge of a shelf.

2. Loop a paper-clip on the elastic band and hang the paper-clip from the drawing pin.

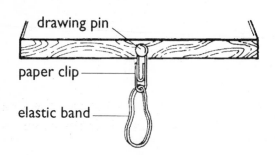

3. Use thin string to make a handle for the yoghurt pot. Tie the handle to the bottom of the elastic band.

4. Fix a ruler to the wall behind the elastic band with adhesive tape.

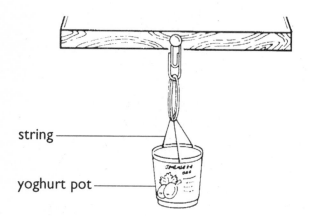

5. Bend a paper-clip to make a pointer and fix it to the elastic band.

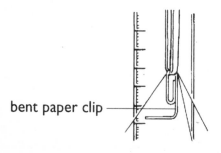

6. Make a mark where the pointer is on the ruler when the cup is empty.

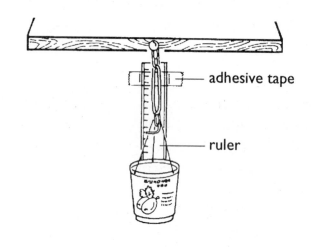

▲ Put a small object, such as a marble, in the yoghurt pot.

Mark how far the elastic band is stretched by the weight.

▲ Try other objects. Do they weigh more or less? If you have some real weights you could use these to see that your balance weighs accurately. Record your results below.

Object	Distance stretched
Marble	

▲ Can you make a weighing machine using a spring instead of an elastic band?

Weighing with a squashed spring

You will need: a large and a small can; a bed spring or thin wire; a cardboard tube; 2p coins or small weights; a ruler.

▲ Make a weighing machine with a spring.

1. If you do not have a large spring make one from some thin wire. Carefully wind the wire around the cardboard tube. Take away the tube and you have a spring!

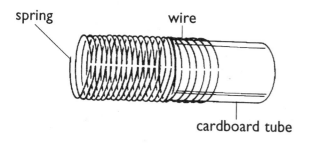

spring   wire

cardboard tube

2. Squash your spring and see how it goes back to its original shape when you let go of it.
3. Put the spring in the bottom of the large can.

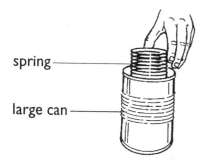

spring

large can

4. Rest the smaller can on top of the spring.

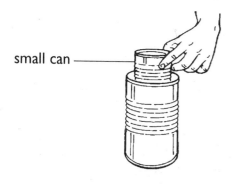

small can

5. Put 2p coins or small weights, one at a time, into the smaller can.

weight

6. Use a ruler to measure how far the small can goes down as the spring is squashed.

▲ Use your weighing machine to weigh small objects.

ruler

Pendulums and swings

You will need: a piece of string 1 metre long; several iron washers or nuts; a clock or a watch with a second hand; a shelf with a hook in the edge; a ruler.

Some old clocks have a pendulum which swings backwards and forwards. It controls the speed of the clock.

▲ Does it make any difference if you alter the length of the pendulum or the weight on the end of it? Conduct this experiment to find out.

1. Tie a heavy iron washer or nut on one end of the piece of string. Tie the other end of the string to the hook.
2. Make your pendulum 60cm long by wrapping some of the string around the hook.
3. Start the pendulum swinging by pulling the washer or nut to one side and then letting it go. Use a clock or watch to time how long the pendulum takes to make twenty swings. (A single swing of the pendulum is when the weight moves from one side to the other and back to where it started.)

4. Repeat the experiment, this time with the pendulum 40cm long. Again see how long the pendulum takes to make twenty swings. Is it more or less than before?
5. Now tie another washer or nut on the pendulum. Make the pendulum 60cm long again, and see how long it takes to make twenty swings. Is it more or less than before?
6. Make the pendulum 40cm long, and see how long it takes to make twenty swings with the extra washer or nut on it. Is it more or less than before?

▲ What does this tell you about pendulums?

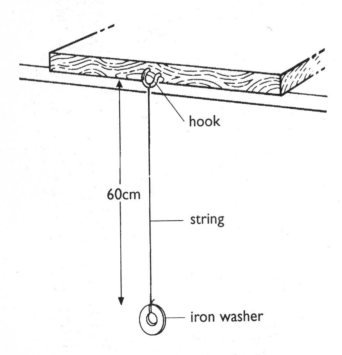

hook

60cm

string

iron washer

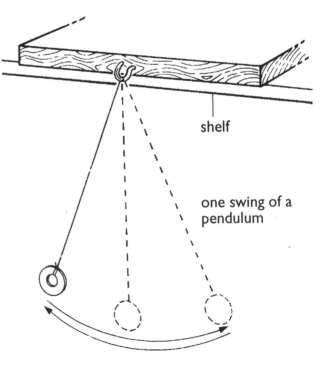

shelf

one swing of a pendulum

Make a wind brake

You will need: cotton reel; string; two paper-clips; ruler; adhesive tape; thin card; scissors; a knitting needle.

▲ Carry out this activity to make a wind brake.

I. Ask an adult to cut four slits at right angles in the cotton reel.

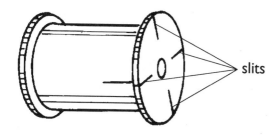

slits

2. Cut a piece of string 40cm long and tape it to the side of the cotton reel.
3. Tie two paper-clips to the end of a piece of string.
4. Put the knitting needle through the centre of the cotton reel.
5. Wind the string around the reel.
6. Hold the knitting needle and watch how fast the string unwinds.

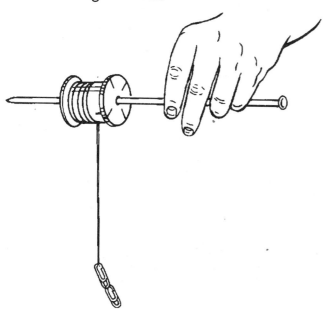

7. Now cut out four pieces of card each measuring 7.5cm by 4cm and push them into the slits in the reel.

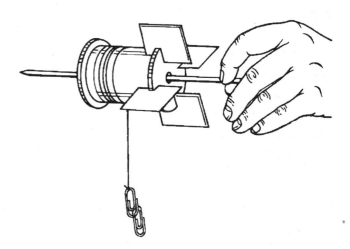

8. Wind the string around the reel again. Hold the knitting needle and watch how fast the string unwinds this time.

▲ Is it faster or slower than before?

▲ Why do you think this is?

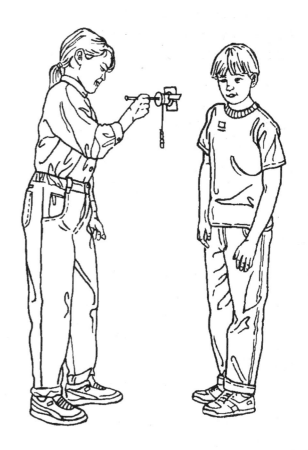

Does size affect a parachute's speed?

You will need: a plastic bin bag; thin string; scissors; two steel washers, both the same size; ruler; a stopwatch or a watch with a second hand.

▲ Does the size of a parachute affect how fast it falls. Conduct this experiment to find out. If possible, carry out this activity in the middle of a playing field or playground, away from windows and overhead wires.

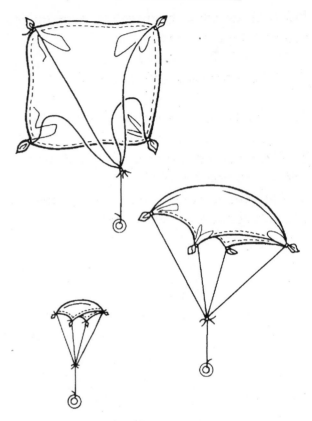

1. Cut eight separate lengths of string about 50cm long.
2. Cut a 30cm square from the plastic bag. Tie a length of string to each corner of the plastic square.
3. Tie the four free ends of the strings together in a knot. Be sure the strings are all the same length.

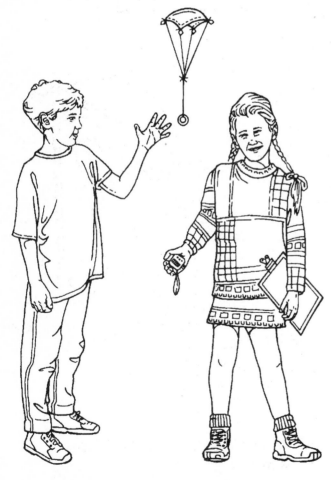

4. Use a piece of string about 10cm long to attach a washer to the knot in the parachute strings.
5. Make a larger parachute using a 60cm square of plastic and the four remaining lengths of string.
6. Attach the washer to the parachute with a 10cm piece of string, as before.
7. To test the parachutes, hold each in the centre of its plastic sheet. Flatten the plastic. Fold the plastic in half. Loosely wrap the string around the folded plastic.
8. Throw the parachutes up into the air one at a time. Use a watch or a stopwatch to time how long it takes for each parachute to reach the ground and record your results.

▲ Does the size of a parachute affect how fast it falls?

▲ Can you explain what is happening?

Measure the force of the wind

You will need: a shoebox; a knitting needle; adhesive tape; scissors.

▲ Make a simple anemometer.

1. Carefully remove the two ends of the shoebox.
2. Cut a curved slot near the end of one side of the box.
3. Push the knitting needle through one end of the box as shown in the picture.

4. Trim one of the box ends that you have cut off the box so that it will make a flap. Tape this on to the knitting needle so that the flap can swing freely.
5. Fix the lid firmly on to the box with adhesive tape.
6. Take the box outside. Stand it so that the flap faces the direction from which the wind is blowing.

The harder the wind blows, the higher it will push the flap.

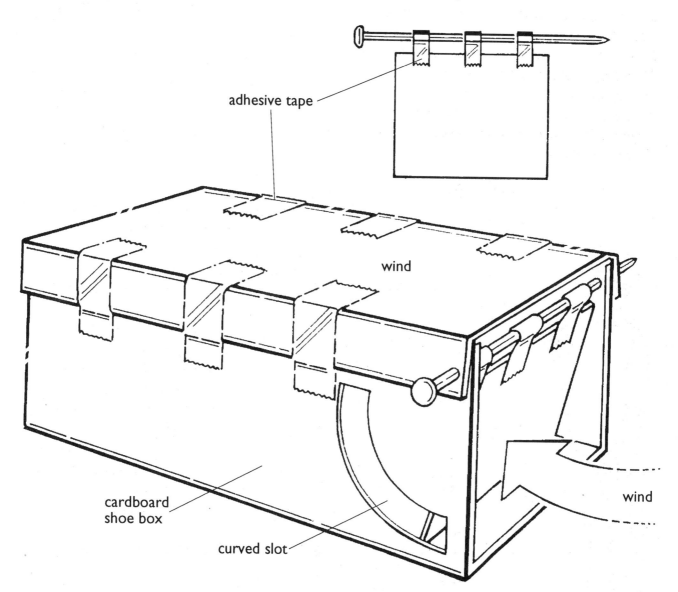

adhesive tape

wind

cardboard
shoe box

curved slot

wind

▲ Can you find a way to make a scale that will let you compare the force of the wind on different days?

▲ How do we make use of the force of the wind?

Is friction useful or a nuisance?

You will need: a pencil.

▲ There are many places on a bicycle where friction acts. Look at the labels on the picture below and complete the chart.

For each one say whether it is important
(a) to have as much friction as possible;
(b) to have as little friction as possible, and explain why.

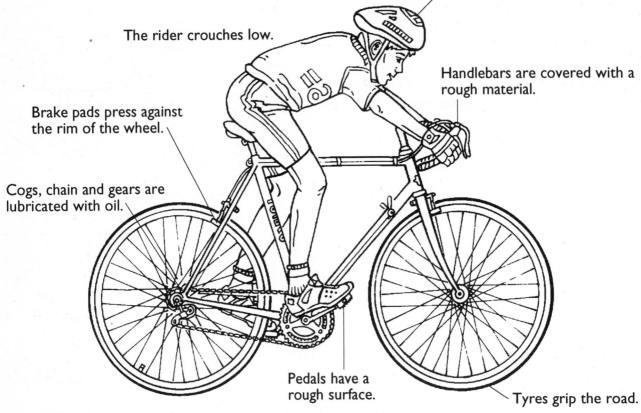

The helmet is streamlined.

The rider crouches low.

Handlebars are covered with a rough material.

Brake pads press against the rim of the wheel.

Cogs, chain and gears are lubricated with oil.

Pedals have a rough surface.

Tyres grip the road.

	(a) As much friction as possible	(b) As little friction as possible	My explanation
Helmet			
Rider			
Brake pads			
Tyres			
Cogs, chain, gears			
Pedals			
Handlebars			

The effect of rubber on friction?

You will need: a small piece of wood, about 14cm by 7cm; a ruler or tape measure; some thick elastic bands; a small hook or screw eye; a spring balance or force meter; a heavy book.

▲ Conduct the following experiment to see what effect rubber has on friction.

1. Screw the hook into the end of the piece of wood.
2. Lay the piece of wood on a smooth table.
3. Fix the hook of the spring balance or force meter to the hook in the wood.
4. What force is needed to make the piece of wood begin to slide along the table? Record your result.

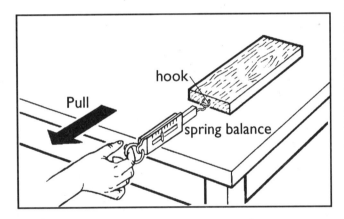

5. Now put three elastic bands around the piece of wood. Use the balance or force meter to see what force is needed to move the piece of wood now. Is it more or less than before?

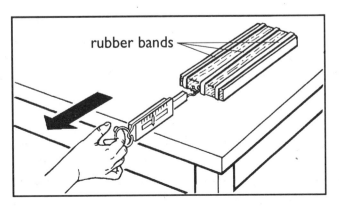

6. Repeat the experiment with a heavy book resting on the piece of wood. Pull the piece of wood along, with and without the elastic bands on it.

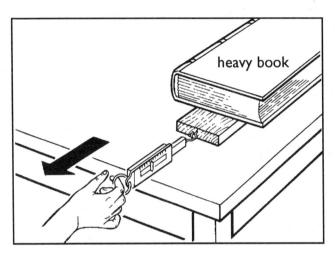

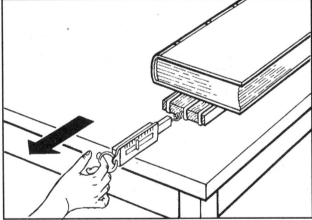

▲ When is the most force needed to move the wood?

▲ Do elastic bands increase or decrease friction?

▲ What happens if you do the experiment with a large stone or a house brick on the piece of wood?

▲ How many ways can you think of in which rubber is used because of the effects it has on friction?

Liquids and friction

You will need: two clean, clear plastic bottles, both the same size; water; washing-up liquid; small tacks, nails or paper-clips.

▲ Do different liquids exert a different frictional force? Conduct this experiment to find out.

1. Fill one bottle with water.

2. Fill the other bottle to exactly the same level with washing-up liquid.
3. Take a tack, nail or paper-clip in each hand. At the same moment, drop one into each bottle.

• Which reaches the bottom of the bottle first?

4. Repeat the experiment nine more times.

• In which bottle do the items usually reach the bottom first?

• In which liquid is there most friction – water or washing-up liquid?

▲ What results do you think you would get if you put treacle, syrup or oil in one of the bottles? Why?

▲ What would be the best way to get the items back out of the bottles?

Can friction be used to warm water?

You will need: a small clean tin can; a thermometer; a block of wood; a tape measure or a piece of tape or rope about 1 metre long; water.

▲ Conduct this experiment to find one of the uses of friction. Ask a friend to help you. Take care when handling the thermometer.

1. Remove the label from the tin can so that it is clean and shiny.
2. Put cold water in the can to a depth of about 1 centimetre.

5. Place the wooden block on top of the can and ask your friend to press down on it firmly.
6. Pull the tape measure, tape or rope quickly backwards and forwards for several minutes (at least 4 or 5).

3. Use the thermometer to take the temperature of the water.
4. Put the tape measure, piece of tape or rope one-half turn around the can.

7. Take the temperature of the water again. Has the temperature changed? By how much?

▲ Where else can you see friction being used to make heat?

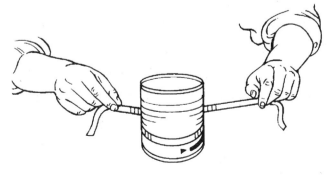

Using rollers

You will need: a piece of string about 60cm long; a large elastic band; two large books; ten round pencils; a ruler.

▲ Do rollers help when moving heavy loads? Conduct this experiment to find out. Work with a friend.

1. Stack the books in the middle of a smooth table.

2. Tie the string around the book at the bottom of the pile.
3. Tie the string to the elastic band.
4. Move the stack of books by pulling on the elastic band.
5. Ask your friend to measure how far the elastic band stretches.
Write the answer here.

_____

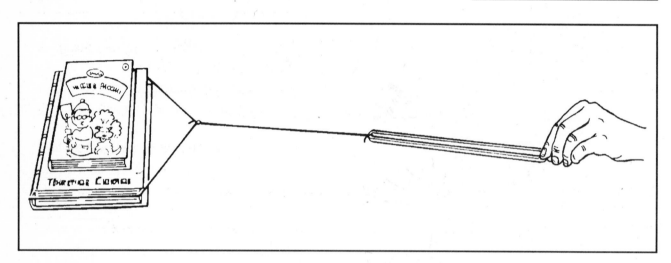

6. Now carefully lay the pencils in a row and put the books on top of them as in the diagram.
7. Move the books by pulling the elastic band. Measure how far it stretches this time. Write the answer here.

_____

▲ Did the band stretch more or less the second time? Can you say why?

▲ What happens if you add a third, smaller book to the pile?

▲ Do the pencil rollers increase or reduce the force you need to move the books?

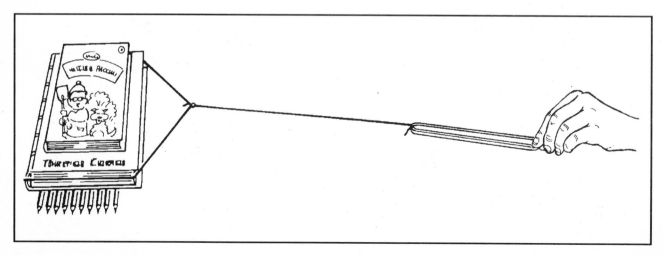

The balloon in a box

You will need: a shoebox; a balloon; scissors; plastic drinking straws; a tape measure.

▲ Conduct the following experiment.

1. Cut a small round hole in one end of the shoebox.
2. Push the neck of the balloon through the hole in the box.
3. Blow up the balloon.

4. Put the box down on a smooth floor.
5. Let go of the neck of the balloon.

• How far does the box travel?

_____

• Where is the force coming from to move the box?

_____

6. Now lay drinking straws across the floor.
7. Blow up the balloon again.
8. Put the box and balloon down on the straws and let go of the neck again.

• How far does the box travel now?

_____

• Is it more or less than before?

_____

▲ What effect do the drinking straws have? Why is this?

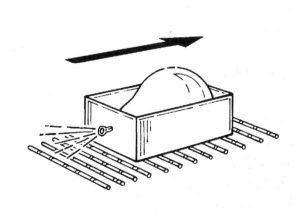

How do ball-bearings help movement?

You will need: two round tins, one of which fits neatly inside the other (cake tins are ideal); ten or twelve ball-bearings or marbles, all the same size.

▲ Do ball-bearings have any effect on friction? Conduct this experiment to find out.

1. Put the smaller tin inside the larger tin.
2. Holding the large tin steady, use the fingers of the other hand to spin the smaller tin round.

• Is it easy or difficult to spin the smaller tin?

3. Now remove the smaller tin and place the ball-bearings or marbles in the bottom of the larger tin.
4. Replace the smaller tin on top of the ball-bearings or marbles and spin it round again.

▲ Is it easier or more difficult than before?

5. Repeat the experiment. This time give the ball-bearings or marbles a thin coating of soap or oil. What difference does this make?

▲ Why are ball-bearings used in the wheels and handlebars of bicycles?

▲ Can you think of any other places where ball-bearings are used?

Floating cans

You will need: an empty cocoa or coffee can, or similar; some clay or Plasticine; a bowl of water; a waterproof marker pen.

▲ Conduct this experiment to see what happens when weights are added to a floating object.

1. Put the empty can in the bowl of water. Does it float? Mark how far the water comes up the side of the can. Mark how far the water comes up the side of the bowl.

2. Put a piece of clay or Plasticine in the can. Does the can float now? What has happened to the water levels?

3. Put more Plasticine in the can. What happens to the water levels?
4. What happens if you put still more Plasticine in the can?
5. Do this experiment again, but this time weigh the empty can and the pieces of clay or Plasticine you put into it.

• What weight of clay or Plasticine will the can hold and still remain floating?

_____

• What weight of clay or Plasticine makes the can sink?

_____

▲ Does a ship float deeper in the water when it is carrying a heavy cargo?

Floating balls

You will need: a small air-filled ball; a large air-filled ball; a bucket; water.

▲ Carry out this activity to find out more about floating objects.

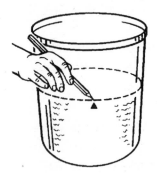
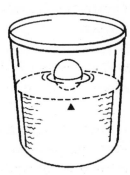

1. Half-fill the bucket with water. Mark the water level.
2. Float the small ball in the water.
3. Now push the ball under the water.

• What do you feel?

• What happens to the level of water in the bucket?

4. Now float the large ball in the water and push it under water.

• What do you feel?

• What happens to the level of water in the bucket?

▲ Which ball did you have to push hardest? Try to explain why.

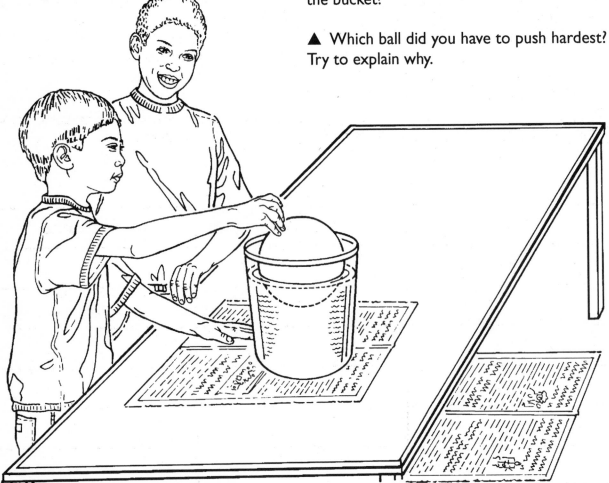

Measuring floating forces

You will need: a spring balance; string; a bowl or bucket half-filled with water; a variety of small objects which will not be damaged by water.

▲ Do objects weigh the same in water as in air? Carry out this experiment to find out.

1. Take one of the objects and weigh it using the spring balance.
2. Record the weight of the object. This is the weight of it in the air.

3. Lower the object on the spring balance into water. Record its weight now.
4. Weigh each of the other objects in air and then in water.

▲ What happened to the weight of the objects in water?

▲ Which object showed the greatest change in weight? Why is this?

Object	Weight in air	Weight in water
tennis ball		

Make a paddle boat

You will need: cardboard; an elastic band; scissors; ruler; a large bowl of water.

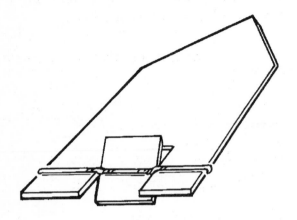

▲ Make a paddle boat from the sheet of cardboard and see how you can make it move forwards or backwards.

1. Cut a square 10cm by 10cm from the cardboard.
2. Cut two corners off the square to make the pointed front of the boat.

3. Cut a square 5cm by 5cm from the rear of the boat.
4. Cut a paddle, 2.5cm by 5cm, from the cardboard.
5. Loop the elastic band over the end of the boat as in the diagram.
6. Insert the paddle between the two sides of the elastic band.
7. Turn the paddle towards you to wind the elsatic band tight.
8. Place the boat in the bowl of water and release the paddle.

• Which way does the boat move?

9. Wind the band in the opposite direction by turning the paddle away from you. Place the boat back in the water and release the paddle.

• Now which way does the boat move?

▲ What is pushing and what is being pushed to make the boat move?

Magnetic forces

You will need: two bar magnets, the objects listed below.

▲ Which of these things will be attracted to a magnet?

    Predict first, then use your magnet to see if you were right.

▲ Record your results on the chart below.

Object	Prediction	Result
2p coin		
10p coin		
ruler		
eraser		
nail		
paper		
paper-clip		
plastic lid		
glass jar		
pin		
pencil		
elastic band		

▲ Discuss your results with a friend.
What materials do you think are magnetic?

When two magnets pull towards each other, they are said to **attract**.
When two magnets push each other away, they are send to **repel** each other.

▲ Find out what happens when you try each of these:

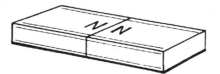

Two North poles adjacent:
repel or attract? _____

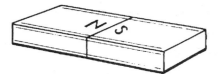

North and South pole adjacent:
repel or attract? _____

South and North poles adjacent:
repel or attract? _____

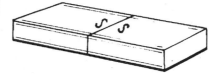

Two South poles adjacent:
repel or attract? _____

▲ Summarise what you have discovered by completing this sentence:

Unlike poles ——————, whereas like

poles ——————.

How strong is a magnet?

You will need: a box of paper-clips; bar magnets of several different sizes; adhesive tape.

▲ Carry out this experiment to find out how strong your magnet is.

1. Tape one of the magnets to a table, making sure that part of the magnet sticks over the edge of the table.
2. Bend open the end of a paper-clip to make a hook. Touch this hook to the end of the magnet that is over the edge of the table.
3. Add other paper-clips one at a time to the paper-clip hook.

• How many paper-clips can you add before they pull loose from the magnet and fall?

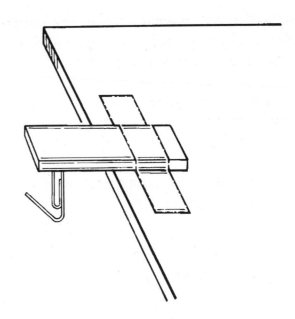

▲ Repeat this activity with other magnets of different sizes.

• Which is the strongest magnet? Is it the largest one?

▲ Are the two ends of a magnet equally strong? Find out.

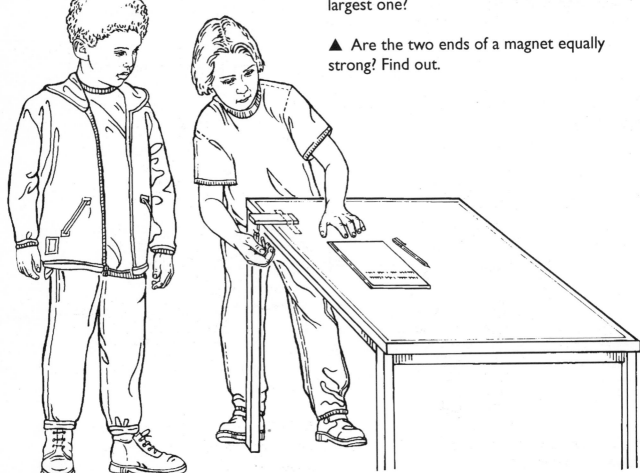

Levers

You will need: an empty treacle or paint tin with the lid firmly on; a coin; a screwdriver; a claw hammer; a nail; a piece of wood.

▲ Do levers help you to open a tin? Find out by carrying out these activities.

Activity 1

1. Try to open the tin using your fingers. Can you do this?

2. Now try opening the tin using a coin. Is it easier? Why?

3. Use the screwdriver to open the tin. How easy was this? Why?

Activity 2

1. Carefully hammer the nail into the piece of wood, so that half of the nail is still above the wood.
2. Can you remove the nail with your fingers?

3. Now use the claw hammer. Is the hammer easier to use than your fingers? Why?

▲ Make a list of objects that act as or use levers, for example a crowbar and a wheelbarrow.

See-saw

You will need: a ruler; 2p coins; a pencil (with flat sides).

▲ How can you make objects of different weight balance?

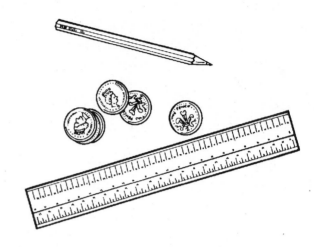

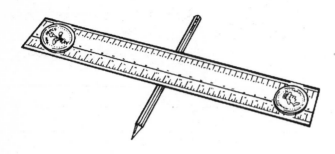

1. Place the ruler on the pencil so that it balances. The pencil acts as a pivot (fulcrum).
2. Place a 2p coin on each end of the ruler until it balances again.

3. Add another coin to one end. What happens? Draw your results.
4. Can you now make the ruler balance without adding another coin? Again, draw your results.

▲ How can you make one coin balance three, four and then five coins?